MAILBOX
Crosswords

A POSTCARD BOOK™　　　　*BY MEL ROSEN*

RUNNING PRESS
PHILADELPHIA, PENNSYLVANIA

Postcard Book™   is a trademark of Running Press Book Publishers.
Canadian representatives: General Publishing Co., Ltd., 30 Lesmill Road, Don Mills, Ontario M3B 2T6.
International representatives: Worldwide Media Services, Inc., 30 Montgomery Street, Jersey City, New Jersey 07302.

9 8 7 6 5 4 3 2 1
The digit on the right indicates the number of this printing.

ISBN 1–56138–161–6

Cover design by Toby Schmidt
Interior design by Christian Benton
Typography: Adobe Garamond, with Futura by COMMCOR, Philadelphia, Pennsylvania.
Printed and bound in the United States by Philadelphia Press.

This book may be ordered by mail from the publisher. Please add $2.50 for postage and handling.
But try your bookstore first!
Running Press Book Publishers
125 South Twenty-second Street, Philadelphia, Pennsylvania 19103

INTRODUCTION

You hold in your hand the world's first collection of Mailbox Crosswords — the newest member of a long succession of brainteasers.

To crossword enthusiasts, December 21, 1913 is a historic date. Small puzzles similar to our modern crossword puzzles first appeared several years earlier, but on that day, Arthur Wynne, composer of rebuses, anagrams, riddles, and other puzzles for the Sunday *New York World,* introduced what he called a "word-cross" puzzle. From then on, puzzle solvers and constructors alike were off and running. By 1925, some crossword books had become best sellers.

Today, crossword puzzles provide mental stimulation and diversion all over the world. In France, Germany, Italy, Spain, Sweden, England, Lebanon, India, and elsewhere, crossword puzzles have evolved locally to accommodate language and tradition. Some puzzles rely solely on general knowledge and vocabulary skills; others also introduce tricks based on sounds and on the mechanics of writing.

This collection of thirty original puzzles is a new way to share the fun. When we travel, our friends and relatives expect to hear from us. Postcards offer a speedy way to honor the obligation; they have only a small space to write in, so we can't spend hours at the task. But these postcards should doubtless keep your message in the recipient's hand longer, and provide some brain exercise in the bargain!

Mel Rosen

P.S.: The puzzle titled "Personal Message" is for your amusement, as well as for a special crossword fancier among your correspondents.

Across

1 *Comique* actor Jacques
5 Get hold of
10 "I Remember _____"
14 Kitchen lure
15 Yo, in a way
16 Writer Kingsley
17 Italian resort
18 Read books?
19 Kind of egg
20 "Last Supper" artist
23 Dey or Anton
24 Asian holiday
25 "The Blue Boy" artist
33 Get _____ hence!
36 Slangy denial
37 Soaring hawk
38 Hammer's musical genre
39 Blaze it in the woods
41 Part of ETA
42 From Donegal
45 Vein's location
46 Consequently
47 "The Last Judgment" artist
50 Noted historical period
51 Expenditures
55 Montmartre artist
62 VPI is one
63 Extruded fiber
64 It's right on the map
65 Rubens subject
66 Happening
67 Baptism, for one
68 Bolshevik's foe
69 Mountain-climber's respite
70 Don't dele!

Down

1 Certain fees
2 So long, along the Seine
3 Ruckuses
4 Period beginning before 1000 B.C.
5 Scorch
6 Sing praises of
7 Actor Ray
8 Rode a toboggan
9 Couch creature?
10 Traditional supernatural force
11 Church corner
12 This and that: Abbr.
13 Italian wine region
21 Santa in California
22 Action word
26 Certain income, for short
27 _____ Jean Baker
28 Toledo's locale
29 Extant
30 Zion's state
31 "The Cotton Club" star
32 It's got plenty
33 In shape
34 Mata _____
35 "Beowulf" is one
40 Iacocca
43 Retreat
44 Submarine
46 Hype artists
48 Victory crown, of old
49 Costello
52 Hallmark
53 "Beau _____"
54 Musical group
55 Apply henna
56 Cross to bear
57 Fed. farming overseers
58 Put aside
59 Looked at
60 Kind of jump or haul
61 Pay to play

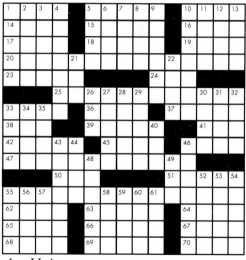

Art Union by Mel Rosen

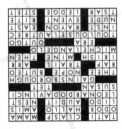

Across

1 Trust
7 On cloud nine
13 Hold fast or tear apart
14 Hologram makers
15 First woman to solo across the Atlantic
17 Grange, for one
18 S.A. range
19 Divests
22 Norm, briefly
23 "Paper or plastic?" item
26 Nice friend
27 Bonn attention-getter
29 Feed to excess
33 Had been
34 1930s boxer Max
36 James or Marilyn
37 Copilot of the first nonstop flight round the world without refueling
40 Rodeo participant
42 Domingo's forte
43 _____ Jima
46 Putting up with
48 Elected ones
49 Cockney cad?
50 Cacophony
51 Common Market initials
53 Wilbur Post's charge
54 Farm buildings
57 Common title word
59 First U.S. licensed woman pilot
64 Win over
65 Surround
66 Nogales nap
67 Certain believers

Down

1 TV brand
2 Shade tree
3 Lecher's looks
4 Bush's alma mater
5 "Metamorphoses" poet
6 Teacher's org.
7 African antelopes
8 Cooking fat
9 North Carolina county
10 Afternoon rituals
11 Miscalculate
12 Summer setting in D.C.
16 Corrode
19 Not processed
20 "_____ little teapot..."
21 Become detached
22 Mets' stadium
23 Impediment
24 From _____ Z
25 Golly!
27 Primitive calculators
28 Accepted rule
30 At full speed, of old
31 Forum finery
32 Resembling: Suff.
35 Type of rug
38 Tight position?

39 _____ the Red
40 Ill-behaved
41 Slugger's stat
44 Tiny
45 Like Father William
47 Biological groupings
52 Founded: Abbr.
53 Office notes
54 Highland hillside
55 Branches
56 Unruly crowd
57 Work on a Strad
58 LP player
59 "For _____ a jolly..."
60 Blackbird
61 So there! in math class
62 Sandwich choice
63 NFL gains

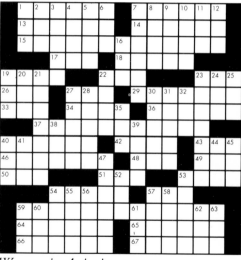

Women in Aviation by Mel Rosen

Across

1 Sothern and Jillian
5 Evidence of infrequent housecleaning
9 Old Nick
14 Boyfriend
15 Fencing blade
16 Psi follower
17 Annoyance on the road
20 Drive
21 Boeing wannabe?
22 Having second thoughts
26 Shoo!
30 Annoyances on the road
36 That was close!
37 There's a lot of them for sale
38 Characteristic
39 Broadcasting
41 By and large
42 Comedienne Fanny
43 Organ stop
46 Coward or Harrison
47 Annoyances on the road
49 Beef quantity
50 Busybodies
52 Sausage holder
56 Gives up
61 Annoyances on the road
65 Spring month
66 Have a bite
67 Monogram detail: Abbr.
68 __ off; measures
69 Twice *quattro*
70 Soap ingredients

Down

1 Fortas and Vigoda
2 Waiting-room call
3 Neck area
4 Of course!
5 _____ Moines
6 Letters on a brown truck
7 Baste
8 Service pieces
9 Tosspots
10 French friends
11 High-schooler
12 Water, south of the border
13 Short snooze
18 Miss the mark
19 Holler
23 Mil. branch
24 Greek letter
25 Advocating
26 Deck hands
27 Twitter
28 High abode
29 "_____-Told Tales"
31 Call _____ day
32 Smiles
33 Asian capital
34 Like some roofs
35 Manner
40 Actor Beatty
41 Isolated hill
43 Spaghetti sauce herb

44 Forbid
45 Select
48 Actress Daly
51 _____-fi
52 Kirk, e.g.
53 Zoning unit
54 Do without
55 Manhattan, Man, etc.
57 Beyond impish
58 Say it isn't so
59 New York canal
60 Fast Atl. crossers
61 _____ relief
62 Infant
63 "Spring ahead" setting, for short
64 Sigma's lead-in

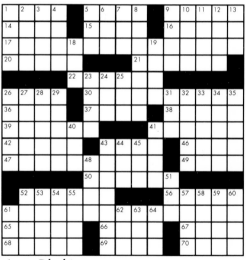

Auto-Phobia by Mel Rosen

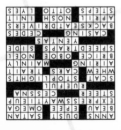

The solved crossword puzzle (shown rotated):

S	A	T	I	N		D	U	S	T		A	N	N	S
Y	A	T	A	I		E	E	R	F		U	A	E	B
A	G	E	M	O		E	E	R	F		P	X	E	
D	U	P		E	I	L	T	Y	A	W	S	S	E	R	P	X	E
	A	N	S	S	E	C		U	A	E	B			
S	T	E	E	R										
			R	U	E	F	U	L						
S	C	A	T		S	T	O	P	L	I	G	H	T	S
I	A	R	T		W	H	E	M		C	A	R	S	
D	A	R			A	I	R	I	N	G				
E	A	M	A	I	N	L	Y							
L	L	E	O	N		E	C	I	R	B				
S	P	E	E	D	T	R	A	P	S		E	D	I	S
			Y	E	N	T	A							
S	E	D	E	C		G	N	I	S	A	C			
B	A	C	K	S	E	A	T	D	R	I	V	E	R	S
A	P	R	I	L		N	O	S	H		I	N	I	T
S	T	E	P	S		O	T	T	O		T	A	V	E	S

MAILBOX CROSSWORDS   A Postcard Book™   © 1992 Running Press Book Publishers

Across

1 Fathers
5 Binge
10 Grand
14 Double-reed instrument
15 "_____ we a pair?"
16 Hold
17 Mild cheese
19 Stir things up
20 Time of day, to a poet
21 Remain
22 Gun the engine
23 Hatch or Kennedy
25 Fragrant solvent
29 Sharply-flavored cheese
31 Arcing shot
32 Bride
35 Photocopy
36 So that's it!
37 Uproar
38 Semisoft cheese
41 French negative
42 "To _____ With Love"
43 Distinct: Pref.
44 Like morning lawn
45 Turkey or cat
46 Soft creamy cheese
50 Display shelving
52 Aaron Burr, for one
56 Fido's warning
57 1989 Heisman Trophy winner
58 Funny Charlotte
59 Roman robe
61 Pungent blue cheese
64 Cut
65 Ersatz expletive
66 Adam's grandson
67 Storied bear
68 Logic
69 Unit of force

Down

1 Sports arenas
2 Higher than
3 "The Dirty _____"
4 _____ you!
5 Tailor, to Tiberius
6 Acquire weapons in advance
7 _____ on; trust
8 Photog. blowup
9 Guess at LAX
10 Plumed bird
11 Smoked cheese
12 Sundial numeral
13 Noncom
18 Filmdom terrier
22 Oscar de la _____
24 Simian
25 Piedmont commune
26 Actor James
27 Not at all
28 Dark heavy wood
30 Bar legally
32 It's often in a basket
33 Dostoyevsky's "The _____"
34 Cheese, on *la lista*
38 Dietary roughage
39 German river
40 Shade of green
44 Dolores _____ Rio
47 Old saws
48 One continent
49 Envisioned
51 Pie chart
53 Dramatic approach
54 Where a do gets done
55 Rag
57 Small songbird
59 Recipe qty.
60 Yoko __
61 "Pygmalion" monogram
62 Chihuahua cheer
63 Letter of the British alphabet

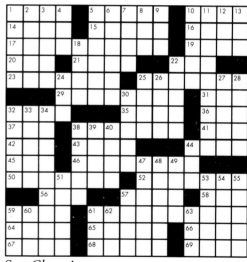

Say Cheese! by Mel Rosen

Across

1 Part of a circle
4 Andy of the comics
8 Where Tintern Abbey is
13 Tijuana water
14 Environmental concern, in brief
15 Crosswise to 45 Across
16 Theda Bara's moniker
17 Do fruitless work
19 One of Pete Rose's mosts
21 Lingerie trim
22 Untested
23 Trust
24 Road curve
26 Laid claim to
30 Cabinet bur.
34 Ensign wannabe
37 Sought office
38 Tightwad
39 Large duck
40 World Series mo.
41 Off-kilter
42 _____-Saxon
43 Common article
44 Sums, with "up"
45 Yacht's stabilizer
46 From that cause
48 14 Across, e.g.
50 Tasty dishes
54 Reverential wonder
57 CSA supporters
60 Mideast land
61 Noble birth claimant
64 Dig for ore
65 Broom of twigs
66 Another 48 Across
67 Roman poet
68 Proverb
69 Vortex
70 1992 Grammy rock group

Down

1 Size of type
2 Dance of Cuban origin
3 Jester's insignia
4 General Aviation plane
5 Herr's sigh
6 Betting combine
7 "Not guilty," for one
8 Salary
9 Olivia d'_____ of "The Wonder Years"
10 Author Uris
11 Sugar-coat
12 Diving duck
13 Grandparental
18 Served with verve
20 Corrida figure
25 Crusader's protection
27 Trifling talk
28 Old buckle
29 Sign up
31 Revue piece
32 Redactor's word
33 Some are fine
34 Mountaintop
35 _____ of fire
36 Brink
38 Provincial dialect
46 All even
47 In a wicked way
49 _____ de menthe
51 Ingenuous
52 Jeans material
53 Olympic coaster
54 1970s Swedish pop quartet
55 Gardener's bane
56 Actress Lanchester
58 Neuwirth of "Cheers"
59 Reported
62 Outfit
63 Steiger or Serling

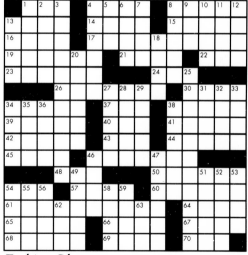

Fashion Plate   by Mel Rosen

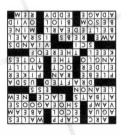

Across

1 Half: Pref.
5 Jazz guitarist Montgomery
8 Fed. agents
12 Typeset *like this*
13 Dance in 3/4 time
15 Greek liqueur
16 Baseless
17 Children
18 Broadcasts
19 July setting in NYC
20 Lost in Accra?
22 Rich
25 Break a commandment
26 Delta makeup
27 Dome style
32 Kind of committee
34 Off-Broadway entertainment
35 Tribulation
36 Gas in a tube
37 Meadow rodents
38 Kitten's cry
39 Draw on
40 Cloys
41 Anwar of Egypt
42 Settle
44 Theater box
45 Uneven?
46 News
49 Refusal to a señor in Oslo?
54 _____ Lanka
55 Riyadh resident
56 Allah's revelations
57 Whitewash
58 Quick reminder
59 Pitchers
60 Auto import
61 Catch sight of
62 _____ Alamos
63 Sir Christopher _____

Down

1 Tendon
2 Chopin piece
3 Where to buy shakes in Valletta?
4 Kind of humor
5 Wishy-_____
6 Four-legged movie star
7 Amaze
8 Beard shape
9 Alaska's _____ Glacier
10 Pound, the poet
11 Prying
13 Isle of _____
14 Fanatical
21 Team
23 6 Down, for one
24 Paramedical treatment, for short
27 Cosmetic colloid
28 Holiday times
29 Chinese food choice in Stockholm?
30 Midwestern state
31 Ancient Briton
32 Before, in combos
33 "Giant" star
34 Coll. mil. program
37 Beard shape
38 Christmas trio
40 _____ cracker
41 Lawn
43 Rodeo performer
44 Legal charges
46 Peter and Nicholas
47 Road slope
48 Audit
49 Nominate
50 Unrefined minerals
51 Highway exit
52 Cheek by _____
53 Popular cookie
57 Crow's cry

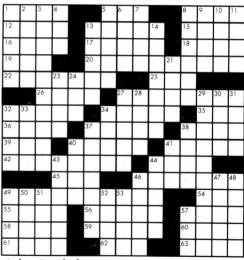

Atlas Smiled by Mel Rosen

Across

1 Keep _____ on
5 Peak experiences
10 Latch onto
14 Orchestral tuning fork
15 The blahs
16 Elcar of "MacGyver"
17 Where to spend francs
20 Acted impolitely
21 Dim
22 Manufacturer's claim
23 Driving necessities
25 Rang out
29 Cribbage scorer
30 Benevolent
34 Intolerant one
35 Length x width
36 Scand. country
37 Where to spend pounds
41 Engine turnover meas.
42 Elec. units
43 Wide awake
44 Go for photos
46 Plea at sea
47 Challenges Boitano
48 Short time period, shortly
50 Technology: Abbr.
51 In a state of wonder
54 Shooting script
59 Where to spend dollars
62 Wing-shaped
63 Accustom
64 From Rome, briefly
65 Exceptional
66 Kathy of "Misery"
67 Zippo

Down

1 Fling
2 Be an accomplice
3 _____ fide
4 Crystal gazer
5 Took charge
6 Family relative
7 No-see-um
8 Attila, for one
9 He starred with Imogene
10 Solidarity city
11 Fence part
12 Not "pro"
13 Tease
18 Biological varieties
19 Cry's partner
23 Adolescents
24 By Jove!
25 Sound from Tweety Pie
26 Silent Marx
27 Agenda details
28 Actor Gibson
29 Flat-bottomed boats
31 Sea arm
32 _____ Dame
33 Mild expletives
35 _____ committee
38 Feature of Hope's profile
39 Assembling
40 Chicken _____ king
45 "The _____ Strikes Back"
47 Play parts
49 Vast amount
50 Twenty
51 A way away
52 Kind of monster
53 Open a bit
54 Close
55 Related
56 Old newspaper section
57 "I knew _____ instant..."
58 Roué's look
60 Pen point
61 Genetic letters

Shopping Spree by Mel Rosen

MAILBOX CROSSWORDS   A Postcard Book™   © 1992 Running Press Book Publishers

Across

1 Yep's opposite
5 Life of a region
10 Mil. wing
14 Catches something
15 Man of the world
16 Rank high
17 Voting group
18 Attend
19 Forehead
20 Indoor roller coaster
23 Walks barefoot
24 "_____ Kampf"
25 Violinist's need
28 Play siren
32 Bible book
33 Protozoan
38 Who _____ you?
39 Famous theme park
42 Sinuous swimmer
43 Put through the paces
44 Farrier's tool
45 Gloomy, to poets
47 Photocopy's predecessor
48 Military meal
51 Economist Smith
53 Park area
58 _____ and now
59 Architectural order
60 Calm under pressure
62 Smell _____
63 Gambol
64 That *femme*
65 Cuts the grass
66 Celebrates
67 Kind of flight

Down

1 Pinch
2 Artist's media
3 Fall heavily
4 Light fiction, for many
5 Having a headquarters
6 List elements
7 Dairy case item
8 Mrs. John McEnroe
9 In unison
10 Polished
11 Graceful gown
12 Like _____ of bricks
13 Not quite several
21 Beverage container
22 Giant
25 Assessed
26 Earth tone
27 Monument
29 "_____, I'm Adam"
30 Not poetry
31 Musical pace
33 License datum
34 Wrong: Pref.
35 Fall mo.
36 Barely manage
37 Speak up at the auction
40 Up _____; cornered
41 Moues
46 Soldiers' org.
47 _____ *de mer*
49 Test the air
50 Put away
51 Get up
52 Levels
53 Plane or space intro
54 Sketch
55 Ohm or erg
56 _____ contendere
57 GI Joe, for one
58 Stage hog?
61 Composer Delibes

Walt's World by Mel Rosen

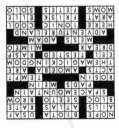

Across

1 Virtuous
6 Mock; taunt
10 Pale
14 Surface
15 "Don't throw bouquets _____"
16 In need
17 Gift from Orlando
20 Back when
21 Gypsy man
22 Certain shoes
23 _____ Plaines
25 Pitcher's stat
26 Gifts from the Caribbean
34 Of a leg bone
35 Sternward
36 Congregated
37 "...a more perfect _____"
38 _____ deco
39 Native Israeli
41 A-E connection
42 "Able was I _____..."
43 _____ up; goes on the wagon
44 Gift from Sanibel Island
48 Seine land
49 Slapstick missile
50 Spine sections
52 Cpl., for one
54 Gal of song
57 Gift from Liberty Island
61 Jo _____ Worley
62 Arab chieftain
63 Jeweled headgear
64 Costly
65 Workout clubs
66 Choir accompaniment

Down

1 _____ Cass
2 First: Abbr.
3 Puerto _____
4 Look into
5 Sidelong glance
6 _____ together; crowded
7 SHAEF sector
8 Ostrich look-alike
9 Aretha Franklin hit
10 Tarzan
11 Daytime TV fare
12 _____ d'oeuvre
13 1993, 1994, etc.
18 Sing in falsetto
19 Dollar lead-in
24 Find with difficulty
26 Snap
27 Tolerate
28 Carioca's home
29 Rocker _____ Halen
30 Frequently
31 It's sometimes burnt
32 _____ Haute
33 RR stops
34 Slow boats
38 Barton's org.
39 Bibber
40 _____ Dhabi
42 Landed holdings
43 Plans, informally
45 More frilly
46 Italian bread?
47 Cruise ships
50 Trig ratio
51 Magnani of film
53 HRE name
54 Kind of party
55 Mystique
56 Slender
57 Fit to be tied
58 Ref's assoc.
59 Estuary
60 Atmosphere

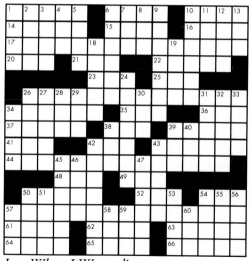

Just What I Wanted! by Mel Rosen

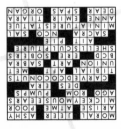

Across

1 Actor Goldblum
5 Opera extra's prop
10 School orgs.
14 Rug type
15 Scout rank
16 Comment from Charlie Chan
17 Biblical idol
19 Pimlico strap
20 "Concorde," e.g.
21 Evened up
22 Pigging out
24 Coal scuttle
25 Alphabetize
26 Relief
30 First Amendment's guarantees
33 Shows appreciation
34 Taunts
35 Profit
36 Height: Pref.
37 Destined
38 Walk on the beach
39 Certain Johnny
40 "The Man Who _____ Be King"
41 Range critter
42 In a meet way
44 In a row
45 Pew sections
46 Actor Cariou
47 Infuriate
49 Make progress
50 Television receiver
53 "When I was _____"
54 Military medal
57 Dish out
58 Layabout
59 Sweat outlet
60 Split wood
61 Campus figures
62 Vaulted recess

Down

1 Sprees
2 Aphrodite's son
3 Sensed
4 Rage
5 Father's title
6 Like clockwork
7 Dated oath
8 Sum total
9 Arbitrated
10 Went one's own way
11 Now, in classical mythology
12 B-boy link
13 Vocal treat
18 Cultural spirit
23 Summer coolers
25 Formed into a circle
26 Cliff line
27 Stress-induced condition
28 Estimate something's antiquity
29 Rickles show, "_____ Sharkey"
30 In an appropriate way
31 Newspapers, radio, TV, and so on
32 Take the helm
34 Frenchmen
37 Kind of medicine
38 Came in first
40 "_____ Only Just Begun"
41 Truckstop
43 Cheated vis-a-vis expense accounts
44 Seesaws, really
46 Cherished
47 Family member
48 "Family Ties" role
49 Srta., in France
50 Word on an octagon
51 I'm all _____!
52 Genealogy diagram
55 Wedding words
56 Belgian resort town

Elementary, My Dear by Mel Rosen

MAILBOX CROSSWORDS   A Postcard Book™   © 1992 Running Press Book Publishers

Across

1 _____ and sound
5 Hue and cry
10 Gad about
14 Clean up copy
15 State off Sicily
16 Just managed
17 Cathedral site
19 Beseeched
20 Wind dir.
21 Aware of
22 Like fingerpainting
24 Vulcan or Pan
25 Climb a rope
26 One of Elizabeth's residences
32 Musical endings
33 Weightlifting exercises
34 It may be common
36 Kind of fall
37 One code
38 Be important
39 Blonde shade
40 Not so important
41 The stuff of life
42 Where to see the Crown Jewels
45 _____ India Company
46 Hot air
47 Deli purchase
50 Elbows
52 Critical
55 Purloined
56 Salisbury Plain wonder
59 Formerly
60 Ticket receipts
61 Put one over on
62 Worker
63 Frets
64 Cooking meas.

Down

1 Made by hand
2 Tennis call
3 Excellent
4 And so on: Abbr.
5 Fixes text
6 Trailing
7 Palo _____
8 Map notation: Abbr.
9 _____ Islands, Pacific group
10 Crawling
11 Tex.'s neighbor
12 Stray
13 Whirlpool
18 Gangsters
23 Otis or Piggy
24 Pesky insect
25 Write hastily
26 Do your _____!
27 Sun Valley state
28 Wild cat
29 _____ the mill
30 Southwest plain
31 Devoured
32 IRS foil, perhaps
35 Former NBA star Unseld
37 Hangs in there
38 Crimson and ruby
40 Gymnastics apparatus
41 Grind teeth
43 Sap
44 Monster
47 Put an end to
48 Top-notch
49 Eccentric, plus
50 Prank
51 Freshly
52 Door adjunct
53 Freudian terms
54 Cry of pain
57 Tit for _____
58 Newt

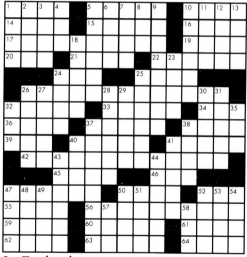

In England by Mel Rosen

Across

1 Dust-ups
5 One Sea
10 South Seas island
14 Sheltered
15 Exploding stars
16 In the sack
17 Huckleberry _____
18 Steve Canyon
20 Kiddies
21 Second notes
22 Purgatories
23 Greek letters
25 Neckline shape
26 Yellowstone feature
28 Map projection
33 Wood sorrel
34 Lebanon tree
36 Destroy gradually
37 Reunion goer
39 Closely packed
41 Concerto flourish
42 In a while
44 Trolley sound
46 Plop or choo lead-in
47 Travel without a ticket
49 Precludes
51 Dance, in France
52 Kitchen cleanser
53 Señoritas, perhaps
57 Nebraska governor
58 Bone-dry

61 Ratso
63 Strong breeze
64 Elvis _____ Presley
65 Say "fo'c's'le"
66 Financial claim
67 Tuna _____ sandwich
68 Ceremonies
69 To the _____ of the earth

Down

1 Transport for 17 Across
2 Medley
3 Thelma and Louise
4 Intuits
5 Spectrum region
6 Auditioner's objectives
7 Currier and _____
8 Noticed
9 Faith follower
10 Soothing stuff
11 Common rhyme scheme
12 Carson successor
13 March time
19 Item
24 Gumshoe
25 Vice _____
26 Hockey scores
27 Showy display
28 Macho
29 Jeanne d'_____
30 Casey Jones
31 More peculiar

32 Brings up
35 Transfer
38 Kitten's call
40 Okays
43 Morocco's capital
45 Precious stone
48 Laundry need
50 Darwin's ship
52 Unrefined

53 Composer Khachaturian
54 "Mondo Cane" theme song
55 Favorite
56 Guy
57 Final notice
59 "_____ Three Lives"
60 Hideaways
62 Actor Wallach

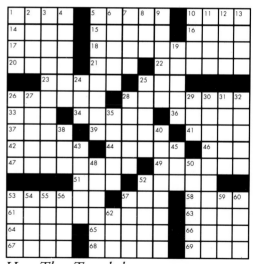

How They Traveled by Mel Rosen

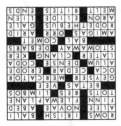

Across

1 Aswan and Hoover
5 Nouveau _____
10 Travels
14 Dies _____
15 Wan
16 Eric of Monty Python
17 Northern epic
18 Largest of the Virgin Islands
20 Soccer tally
21 Nonsense
22 Alice Kramden, _____ Meadows
23 Containing carbon
25 Zilch
26 Busy as _____
27 Largest of the Balearic Islands
32 Distance-weight-time syst.
34 Kiri Te Kanawa soli
36 Litigants
37 Puerto _____
39 Day, to Dali
40 Who _____?
41 Tocsin
43 Ne'er-do-well
46 Oriental sash
47 Lesser Antilles isle
49 John Stuart _____
51 Lepidopterist's gear
52 Seasoned stews
55 Family member
59 Play on words
60 Pack away
61 Island Columbus visited in 1492
63 Hibernia
64 Toast topper
65 Bay
66 Sub _____; quietly
67 Attention-getting sound
68 Solti's reading matter
69 Fit of pique

Down

1 San _____, California
2 Passion
3 Island off Africa
4 Underwater experiment site
5 More grating
6 Stern or Asimov
7 Casino disc
8 Female lobster
9 Involve
10 Prepare for battle
11 Repute
12 Author Wiesel
13 Alluring
19 Weeds out
24 PBS benefactor
25 Twangy
27 Household helpers
28 Yes, to Yves
29 Island off New Zealand
30 Exam taker's notes
31 _____ spumante
32 Horseshoe, for one
33 Arizona river
35 Dolt
38 Majestic sphere
42 Fad out of hand
44 Stem from
45 Fix a result
48 "_____ the Menace"
50 Also-rans
52 Yardstick
53 Human trunks
54 Work out
55 Cut down
56 Lubricates
57 Employs
58 "Out, out, damned _____!"
59 Marco _____
62 Bus. abbr.

Geography Lesson by Mel Rosen

Across

1 Unfriendly
5 Revenue category
10 Kind of job
14 African lily plant
15 Softly, to Solti
16 Trend
17 Field hand
18 Orch. need
19 Greenpeace's concern, in brief
20 . . .at a fraternal convention
23 Pixy
24 Edge
25 Downcast
28 Poker chip
31 Prehistoric monument of Britain or France
36 Compass pt.
37 Ceremonial feast
39 Sheer linen fabric
40 . . .in the Foreign Legion
44 *Pomme de __* (potato)
45 Story
46 Social insect
47 Central New York lake
49 Worn out
51 Possesses
52 Merchandise: Abbr.
54 Second quality, for short
56 . . .as musicians
65 Cathedral projection
66 Marine menace of old
67 Filet
68 Educator Horace
69 Thirst for
70 Newts
71 Thin piece of wood
72 Like some seals
73 Twosomes

Down

1 Limits
2 Margarine
3 Diving bird
4 Thick
5 In a natty fashion
6 "_____ We Got Fun?"
7 Whip
8 Put on record
9 Seamy
10 Holy women (Fr.)
11 Appealing
12 Smell
13 Shoe seam
21 Getting up there
22 Overact
25 Brief brawl
26 Livid
27 Plow name
29 Become
30 Erie, for one
32 Ferrigno
33 Hebrew prophet
34 Dorsey hit, "Maria _____"
35 Cozy homes
38 Citrus fruit
41 Part of TGIF
42 Shelf
43 Withdrew from office
48 Offer as an example
50 Affirmative side
53 Negev native
55 Like a judge on the bench
56 Sweet potatoes
57 Gem of Australia
58 Annapolis inst.
59 Pay a flat fee
60 Outcry
61 Church area
62 Bean curd
63 Sondheim's "_____ the Woods"
64 Capone's nemesis

Laurel and Hardy by Mel Rosen

Across

1 Certain Balkan
5 1980 Cara film
9 Roberts of Tulsa
13 Nostalgic song
14 One-on-one fight
15 Starlet's dream
16 1975 Pacino film
19 Bathing suit name
20 Moved furtively
21 Barrier
24 Hill dweller
25 1957 Hope film
31 Business arrangements
35 Greet the day
36 Salt Lake City student
37 Marble
38 Jeweler's weight
39 B&O stop
40 Yellowish brown shade
42 Sugary ending
43 45 inches
44 Merchandise
45 Fits closely together
48 1974 Bronson film
50 The Tin Man's request
52 Mariner's dir.
53 Assimilated
57 Marathon finish line
63 1954 Brando film
66 Velocity
67 Tabriz's land
68 Grosbeak
69 Scout's snarl
70 Faction
71 Team of oxen

Down

1 Feed the pigs
2 Sidle
3 Sally in space
4 Draw a _____ on
5 Govt. safety org.
6 _____ Wiedersehen
7 NYC team
8 Actress Verdugo
9 Rococo
10 Chess piece
11 Medicinal plant
12 Work a loan
13 _____ bodkins!
17 Luke Skywalker's teacher
18 Break up
22 Entertained
23 Dispositions
25 Breakfast staple
26 Show you're human?
27 Buenos _____
28 Dos Passos trilogy
29 767, for one
30 Place for underwater tests
32 Desktop computer brand
33 Some are great
34 Taffeta sound

40 Elec. meter readout
41 Hee-_____
46 Place mentioned in Jeremiah 7:31
47 Locale
49 Region: Abbr.
51 _____ and Clark
53 Ireland county
54 _____ even keel
55 Preminger
56 Virginia _____
58 Not certain
59 Con _____; lively, in music
60 Cosh
61 "_____ upon a time..."
62 Utmost degree
64 Toe preceder
65 Doorway: Abbr.

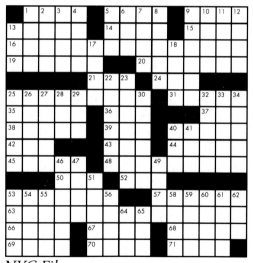

NYC Films by Mel Rosen

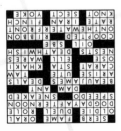

MAILBOX CROSSWORDS   A Postcard Book™   © 1992 Running Press Book Publishers

Across

1 Choose in November
5 Town square
10 Coif style
14 Noble title
15 Mooed
16 Lack
17 Pigged out
20 Mao _____-tung
21 Genesis shepherd
22 Odd traits
23 Potent potables
24 Sacrifice, often
25 Ices down
28 Sighing word
29 Clock setting at long. 0
32 Eagle's nest
33 Premed. course
34 Crop
35 Pigged out
38 Sawbucks
39 Disarray
40 Speed
41 Chemical suffix
42 With skill
43 Up for the day
44 Stock exchange asset
45 Con game
46 Cat
49 Bodily pouches
50 High dudgeon
53 Pigged out

56 Iraq's Shatt-Al-_____
57 Hobbled
58 Burglar of a sort
59 Not so much
60 Beethoven's "*Für* _____"
61 Former spouses

Down

1 Suit unit
2 Filly fillers
3 Loyal
4 Sprite
5 Academy frosh
6 Abundant stores
7 Mil. offense
8 Buddhist sect
9 Okay but not great
10 Not suited
11 Shapely fruit
12 Knock down
13 Lyric poems
18 ". . . _____ and I can't get up!"
19 Stars
23 Police blotter entry
24 The _____; boredom
25 Saguaros
26 _____ of Troy
27 Debbie Reynolds revival
28 Eager and nervous
29 Suburbanite's pride
30 Photo finish

31 'Twixt's partner
33 Mature
34 Prospector's filing
36 Besiege
37 Clause's relative
42 Lo-o-o-o-ng time
43 Give in
44 Pigs
45 Targets for 58 Across

46 Mexican gemstone
47 Remedy
48 Airport abbrs.
49 Half: Pref.
50 Mountain goat
51 Storm
52 _____ Benedict
54 Shakespearean prince
55 Use Rit

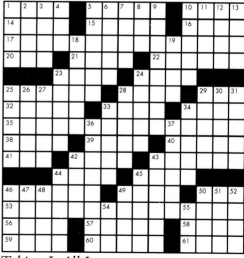

Taking It All In by Mel Rosen

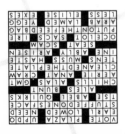

Across

1 Lugosi
5 Singer LaBelle
10 Memo
14 Sharif of film
15 Steer clear of
16 "Terrible" ruler
17 WHAT THIS IS NOT
20 Dark horses
21 Assists
22 Mach 1 exceeder
23 Shadow box
25 Frighten
29 Tasteful quality
31 Moo's relative
34 IRS threats
36 Breech
37 Religion offshoot
38 WHAT THIS IS
41 Spock's boss
42 Lamb's dam
43 Stuns
44 Offspring
45 Discussion group
47 Publish
48 _____ and crafts
49 Here: Fr.
51 Milieu for 41 Across
54 "Enterprise," for one
59 WHAT THIS REPLACES
62 Chip in
63 Separate

64 Spoken
65 Rosary unit
66 Carwash step
67 Habit

Down

1 Hits with a short punch
2 Runner Zatopek
3 Lingerie trim
4 TV's Johnson
5 Cuts back
6 Wards off
7 Goes one better
8 Pedro's uncle
9 Psyche parts
10 More precise
11 Track shape
12 Diamond cover
13 Pass catchers
18 Knocks over
19 _____ she blows!
23 French fighter plane
24 Dad
25 Flour containers
26 Relic
27 Decorate
28 Be daring
30 Reach accord
31 Ruth of "Laugh-In"
32 Steve or Ethan
33 Nuclear trial
35 Work out

37 Gangland boss
39 Possesses
40 Baseball bigshot
45 Bird of _____
46 Cola-bottle measures
48 Twinged
50 À la _____
51 Clean the deck
52 Evergreen tree

53 Movie dog
54 Avon's bird
55 Spectacle
56 Medal winner
57 Mideast country
58 Hide
60 Paddle
61 News org.

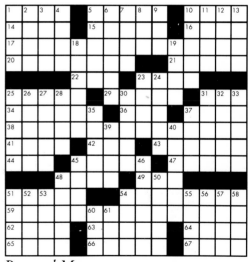

Personal Message by Mel Rosen

Across

1 Open and _____ case
5 Ankles
10 Switch settings
14 Sugar-coat
15 Fake name
16 Cut back
17 British inventor of the concertina
19 Quaker's pronoun
20 Tell
21 Wanted
23 _____ capita
24 Abrasive mineral
25 Influenced
29 Long garment
32 Had concerns
33 Yellow vehicles
34 Owns
37 Circle segments
38 Avis competition
39 Garage employee, for short
40 Speedometer's meas.
41 Shakespeare edition
42 Like some TV time
43 Winter spike
45 Observed Lent
46 The _____ and the Papas
48 Sample
49 Put on notice
52 Asleep at the switch
57 Know-nothing
58 Russian chemist who established periodic law of elements
60 Throat-clearing sound
61 Concepts
62 Actress Raines
63 Church service
64 Tilted
65 TV's "_____ of Our Lives"

Down

1 Put Singer to use
2 Sunken fence
3 Consumer
4 Eyewash
5 Took a little
6 Tailor
7 _____ Grande
8 True grit
9 Oh!
10 Best conditions
11 German thermometer improver
12 Less restrained
13 Run-down
18 Not live
22 Stage scenery
25 Flimflam
26 Speed factor in "Star Trek"
27 Greek inventor of a certain screw
28 Approving word
29 French discoverer of radium
30 Regarding
31 Tasseled topper
33 Clock chime, at sea
35 Summit
36 Throw off
38 Ad _____ committee
39 Wife's honorific
41 Stallone film
42 Kind of bull
44 Ricochets
45 Most excellent
46 Respectful form of address
47 Hawaiian howdy
48 Khartoum's country
50 Jannings of film
51 Avalon's 1958 hit, "_____ Dinah"
53 Unwanted plant
54 "The Plains of Passage" heroine
55 Swear by
56 Peron and Gabor
59 Educ. soc.

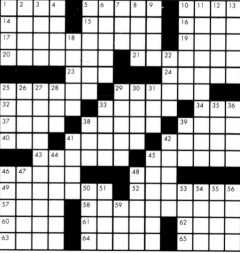

Scientific Study by Mel Rosen

Across

1 Fashionable
5 Helicopter part
10 Most excellent
14 One and the other
15 Gloss over
16 Tibetan monk
17 Chanel
18 Clean the windshield
19 State with conviction
20 Have fun on the waterfront
23 Core of one Chinese philosophy
24 Lots of extras
25 Have fun at the shore
33 Blunt-nosed rodent
34 Day or Duke
35 Get one's goat
36 Choler
37 Divest
38 Scatter seeds
39 Poetical adverbs
41 Water animal
43 Asset
44 Enjoy a restful moment
47 Sighing word
48 Plethora
49 Gather stuff for a display case, maybe
56 Utter
57 Jeweler's gadget
58 Kansas canine
60 Valley
61 Of an ear part
62 Author Hunter
63 Shampoo additive
64 Announces jacks or better
65 Actor Enriquez

Down

1 Network north of the border
2 Owl's comment
3 Yen
4 Laugh exultantly
5 Sequoia
6 Olive genus
7 Quarrel
8 Essence
9 Diets
10 Blurt out
11 Chalet feature
12 "Peter Pan" baddie
13 Popeye or Bluto
21 Acorn's future
22 Kind of story
25 "When you _____ tulip..."
26 Watchful
27 Contragate name
28 Hackneyed
29 Caches
30 Usher's milieu
31 Influence
32 Cuts down
33 Two cents' worth
40 Triangle category
41 Role for James Earl Jones
42 Gridiron backs
43 Liturgical book
45 "2001" computer
46 Maiden-name indicator
49 Select from a group
50 Mountain: Comb. form
51 Chicken's place
52 Idiot box
53 Bridge
54 "I _____ a Parade"
55 Ollie's partner
56 Norman's org.
59 Inside post position

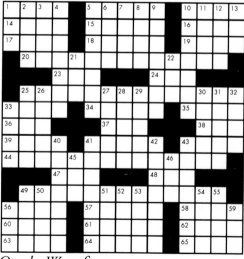

On the Waterfront by Mel Rosen

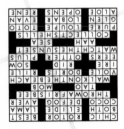

Across

1 Chem. or biol.
4 Put away
8 Sternward
13 Bill's partner
14 Asia _____
15 Blair of films
16 Show-off on the slopes
18 Barbecue locale
19 Specter
20 Affecting the physical body
22 Part of YMCA
23 Add beauty to
24 Certain Olympic competitions
30 Clio contenders
33 Shake off
34 Exclude
35 Arrests
37 Transportation to Oz?
40 Inventor's start
41 Rosary prayer
42 Wee drink
43 Another Olympic competition
49 Mensa candidate
50 Heart
54 Armor plates
56 They may be cellular
58 Mideast dances
59 Route to the top
61 Roar
62 Does one's part
63 Iron source
64 English dandies
65 Seagirt land
66 Comic Louis

Down

1 Indistinct vowel
2 Brewer Adolph
3 Specks
4 Word with flown or handed
5 Gerund finish
6 Common contraction
7 Mistakes
8 Guanaco's cousin
9 Olympic event
10 One opposed
11 Svgs.-guarantee program
12 "The Way"
14 Good word
17 Parking lot mishap
21 Wire measure
23 Targets for Jim Kelly
25 Author Levin
26 Attitude
27 Arabian Sea country
28 South of France
29 Cut it out!
30 Etcher's fluid
31 Fuddy-duddy
32 Passel
36 Cross-country skiing
37 Veteran sailors
38 *Aves* lay them
39 Kind of room
44 Bank jobs
45 Hostelry
46 Soapberry family tree
47 Bibbers
48 EPA's concern
51 Tear jerker?
52 Prepare certain beans
53 Cosmetician Lauder
54 London district
55 College fixture
56 Weapon for Colonel Mustard
57 Day fractions, in brief
58 FDR's successor
60 " _____ in the Family"

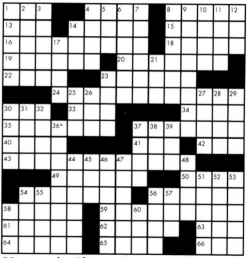

Hitting the Slopes by Mel Rosen

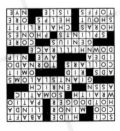

MAILBOX CROSSWORDS   A Postcard Book™   © 1992 Running Press Book Publishers

Across

1 Story's point
5 Coop cry
9 College group
13 Karenina
14 _____ and Gower Champion
15 Lose one's heart to
16 Twosome
17 Oriental
18 Sir Anthony
19 Arizona region
22 1773 jetsam
23 Gunfire
24 Brief outline
28 Dogpatch dad
31 Low spot in California
33 Western alliance: Abbr.
36 Church section
37 Health resort on Lake Geneva
38 One and _____
39 Came upon
40 Arizona gorge
42 Disorganized
43 Holm oaks
44 Cast member
47 Hgt.
48 Utah feature
54 Desolate
55 Banish
56 GI no-show
59 "_____ In a Lifetime"
60 Respond at an arraignment
61 Put one's trust in
62 Use a hoe
63 Perfect scores for Louganis
64 Shoe preserver

Down

1 Cumberland, for one
2 Actress Balin
3 Use scissors
4 Ancient Irish capital
5 Rigatoni or linguini
6 Pennsylvania city
7 Old expletive
8 Hang fire
9 Succulent
10 Cowboy carnival
11 Turn one's eyes
12 Camping needs
14 Tactical actions
20 Longing
21 "Words At Play" author
24 A Cartwright
25 Cartoon skunk _____ Le Pew
26 New York river
27 Roadway: Abbr.
28 Roman scholar
29 "When I was _____"
30 Wrote, but not in ink
32 Gardner and namesakes
33 Cameo stone
34 Amaryllis family plant
35 Thesaurus entries: Abbr.
38 Indefinite pronoun
40 Nickname for Hamlet's mom, perhaps
41 Canadian prov.
42 Cried out
44 Shining
45 Hag
46 Canonical hour
47 Ayn's shrugger
49 Equinox mo.
50 Spindle
51 Claim
52 Go-_____
53 Pitcher
57 Señor's "Hurrah!"
58 Soap ingredient

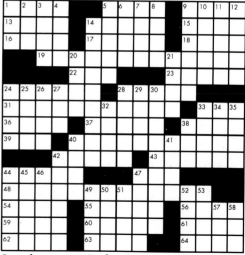

Southwestern Sights by Mel Rosen

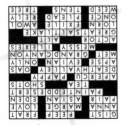

MAILBOX CROSSWORDS   A Postcard Book™   © 1992 Running Press Book Publishers

Across

1 Chastisement from Caesar
5 Indulges to excess
10 Actress Madeline
14 Nerd
15 Action locale
16 Bassoon's relative
17 Metrical foot
18 Opportunist's luck
20 Olympian's blade
21 Druggist's bible: Abbr.
22 Some are obtuse
23 Reverend
25 Family members
26 Was disobedient
28 Patched up, in a way
33 _____ we having fun, yet?
34 "Call Me _____"
36 Instant
37 Viva _____
39 River of Canada and Alaska
41 Biblical prophet
42 Sorcery system
44 Cancún coins
46 Lodge member
47 Phrased another way
49 Brings to a stop
51 VCR button
52 Location
53 Slim
57 Actress Busch
58 Jalopy

61 Efficiency experts
63 _____ facto
64 Osiris's wife
65 Toys for a breezy day
66 Tennis props
67 Set premiums
68 Use a shovel
69 Sand

Down

1 Actress McClurg
2 Box in
3 Watches
4 Optimistic
5 "_____ Night Fever"
6 Make an appearance
7 Short-term office worker
8 Opp. of WSW
9 Low bow
10 King _____
11 Genesis shepherd
12 Leg wear
13 Costner role
19 Atlas detail
24 GOP foe
25 Interoffice papers
26 Enjoy fully
27 Look into
28 Encrusted, as with dirt
29 Gun lobby
30 Boxing official
31 *Étudiant*'s place

32 Office furniture
35 Made a fool of
38 Ingest
40 _____ oblige
43 Sword handles
45 Tampico title, for short
48 Pinches
50 Throbbing
52 Trimmed

53 Pokey
54 Passport notation
55 Radiate
56 _____ majesty
57 "... I _____ man with seven wives"
59 Italian wine center
60 Put in the mail
62 Big shot

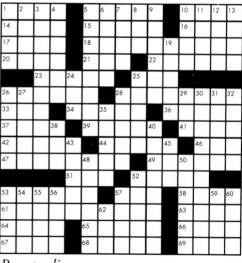

Punctuality by Mel Rosen

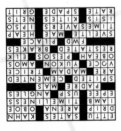

Across

1 O.T. book
5 Séance sounds
9 Ersatz money
14 Bangkok resident
15 Relative of etc.
16 Fast's partner
17 Silent signals
18 Kind of dancer
19 Play a part
20 Agency service
23 Home transactions
24 It may be the limit
25 Footlike part
26 More, to Manuel
27 Watch pocket
30 South Seas spots
34 Flying overseers, for short
35 Bunyan's ox
36 Agency service
40 "Look _____, I'm as helpless . . ."
41 Are you a man _____ mouse?
42 TV awards
43 Once around the track
44 Ballston _____, New York
45 Feather piece
47 Hydrocarbon suffix
48 Balcony
52 Agency service
57 Fragrance
58 Take something off
59 Silent
60 Sleeping bag insulation
61 Talented
62 Foil's alternative
63 Abrasive stuff
64 Army meal
65 Actress Laura

Down

1 Mediterranean volcano
2 Church group
3 Core staff
4 Has trouble with esses
5 Entertain
6 Makes amends
7 Senate runners
8 Dime's place
9 Casual wear
10 Selfsure
11 Method of learning
12 Who _____?
13 Corrals
21 Temporary setback
22 Asimov
26 Chinese revolutionary
27 Rural spot
28 Follow orders
29 Porgy's love
30 Typeset *thusly*. Abbr.
31 Mex. miss
32 Reading _____
33 Actress Arden
34 _____ Angelico
35 Ne'er-do-well
37 Runs easily
38 Bikini top
39 Center
44 Sly
45 Inclines
46 Speaks out
47 Suit of mail
48 Extended family
49 Set sights
50 Small auto
51 Come in!
52 Birthday tradition
53 Saroyan title character
54 Lasso
55 Soft cheese
56 Witnessed

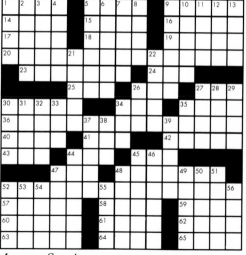

Agency Services by Mel Rosen

MAILBOX CROSSWORDS   A Postcard Book™   © 1992 Running Press Book Publishers

Across

1 Art movement
5 _____ of directors
10 Charity
14 Physical
15 Domed home
16 Call up
17 Astaire/Rogers' first screen teaming, 1933
20 "_____, we have no..."
21 Novelist James
22 Notorious in the extreme
23 Roulette bet
24 "Streetcar" role
25 Skunk in "Bambi"
28 Turn of mind
29 Bilko's rank: Abbr.
32 Catch a dogie
33 Wheels of fortune?
34 Bit of color
35 Kelly/Caron/Levant, 1951 (with "An")
39 "Our _____ in Havana"
40 They're given at birth
41 Remove
42 Nav. rank
43 Uses a straw
44 River of India
46 Clutter
47 Add to the staff
48 Whom credits credit
51 Venetian official
52 Drag off
55 Crosby/Lamour/Hope, 1940
58 Kind of room
59 Orange variety
60 Former British protectorate
61 Honeybunch
62 Edberg or Ekberg
63 Basis

Down

1 Be spiteful
2 Wheel-to-wheel shaft
3 Hours and hours
4 What _____, a mindreader?
5 Having more bulk
6 Poet Nash
7 _____ vera
8 Melee
9 Generous gift
10 Decorate
11 Milan moolah
12 Common street name
13 Vending machine feature
18 Central hall in a church
19 Dept. of _____
23 Vase-shaped pitcher
24 Interstate rigs
25 Picture border
26 Storied shoe salesman
27 Readies for business
28 Grape holders
29 Gesture of futility
30 Fashion
31 Trials
33 Parlor illuminators
36 Flyer of a sort
37 Military vehicles
38 Tiptop
44 Tehee
45 Territory
46 Fashions
47 Used a strop
48 Sinai dweller
49 Ice cream holder
50 London gallery
51 Seedy bar
52 Kind of list
53 Popular cookie
54 Departed
56 Timber splitter
57 Normal result

Travel Films by Mel Rosen

D	A	D	A		B	O	A	R	D		A	L	M	S
E	X	A	M		I	G	L	O	O		D	I	A	L
F	L	Y	I	N	G	D	O	W	N	T	O	R	I	O
Y	E	S		A	G	E	E		A	R	R	A	N	T
			E	V	E	N		S	T	A	N			
F	L	O	W	E	R		V	E	I	N		S	G	T
R	O	P	E			L	I	M	O	S		H	U	E
A	M	E	R	I	C	A	N	I	N	P	A	R	I	S
M	A	N		N	A	M	E	S			O	U	S	T
E	N	S		S	I	P	S		G	A	N	G	E	S
			M	E	S	S		H	I	R	E			
A	C	T	O	R	S		D	O	G	E		T	O	W
R	O	A	D	T	O	S	I	N	G	A	P	O	R	E
A	N	T	E		N	A	V	E	L		A	D	E	N
B	E	E	S		S	W	E	D	E		R	O	O	T

Across

1 Help a crook
5 Cookie cutters
9 Turtles' bills
14 Appointment
15 Not busy
16 Hindu nobleman
17 Former tennis great
18 Baby powder
19 Speechify
20 Celebrate
23 Quasi-medical attn.
24 Go a-courting
25 Miller and Sothern
26 That man's
27 Galena and bauxite
28 Kind of session
31 Gospel keyboard
34 Ad award
35 Hawaiian island
36 Formals
39 Inferior
40 Wise to
41 Fragrant shrub
42 Was in session
43 Anne-de-Beaupré, Thérèse, etc.
44 Rooter
45 Canned meat product
46 Tavern
47 Change color
50 Infrequently
55 Ignited again
56 Drudgery
57 Water, to Juanita
58 Construction machinery
59 Part of RPI
60 Pinballer's bane
61 _____ in on; focussed
62 The luck of the Irish
63 Distant: Pref.

Down

1 Keep up with the times
2 _____ metabolism
3 Work _____
4 High-schooler
5 Me-too remarks
6 Whence many potatoes
7 Model Macpherson
8 Parochial
9 Sears
10 Brings down
11 Slightly open
12 Padua shrew
13 Molt
21 Package cord
22 _____ a kind
26 Bowler and boater
27 Bread spreads
28 Lockup
29 Psychic's sight
30 This and that: Abbr.
31 Questioning birds?
32 Daughter of Uranus
33 Point
34 Of movies
35 Principal
37 Giant
38 Emergency signal
43 Got under someone's skin
44 Shortcomings
45 French river
46 Utter happiness
47 Range critter
48 _____ be sorry!
49 Related to mother
50 Mus. group
51 Stout's Wolfe
52 _____ up; refuse to talk
53 Tibia or fibia
54 Helm or Dillon

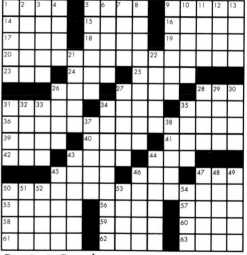

Patriotic Puzzle by Mel Rosen

Across

1 Math subject
5 Gaiters
10 Unlively
14 Smidgen
15 Bottle on a salad bar
16 Sitar melody
17 _____ and void
18 Hair coloring
19 Port of Algeria
20 Wyoming locale
23 Geologic time divisions
24 Hwys.
25 Zoo curiosity
28 It may be nuclear or solar
33 Altar-ego words?
34 Having least importance
40 Had on
41 New Mexico locale
44 Cathedral area
45 Deep blue
46 Do-it-yourself set
47 USX product
49 Matlock matters
51 Pussycat's companion of poetry
54 Relative of a tor
56 New York Harbor sight
64 Mountain, in combos
65 Son of Abraham and Sarah
66 Big shot
67 Corporation VIPs
68 Change coloring again
69 Spock, McCoy, Uhuru, Sulu, and all the rest
70 Berry and Murray
71 One code
72 Hankerings

Down

1 Like Tim
2 Libertine
3 _____ have to do
4 Irritated
5 Unstressed vowel
6 Decrease?
7 Mame, for one
8 Choir voice
9 Small table
10 _____ in the bucket
11 _____ avis
12 Seaweed product
13 Riverside
21 Some tests
22 Second sight
25 Typesetting measures
26 Change as necessary
27 Scandinavian
29 Chit word
30 Operates
31 Tennessee _____ Ford
32 Musical symbols
35 Kimono sash
36 Pale

37 "Kookie" Byrnes of old TV
38 Physics, e.g.
39 Child's game
42 Actor Majors
43 Lexicon: Abbr.
48 Gehrig
50 Model's employer, really
52 Unusual
53 Schlemiel
54 Potter's inventory
55 Cereal grasses
56 Clobber
57 Picnic umbrella
58 Eternity
59 Throw
60 Lose freshness
61 Steak preference
62 Fed. investigators
63 Evergreen shrubs

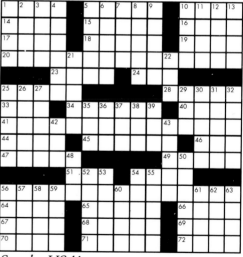

See the USA! by Mel Rosen

Across

1 Never!
6 Schools of whales
10 Mythical cherub
14 Declaim
15 Medley
16 Slangy turndown
17 Clothes
18 "Agriculture and Commerce"
20 Wimbledon's Arthur
21 Ritter of song
22 Monetary claims
23 Emcee's forte
26 Straw house resident
27 Do-it-yourself dish
29 Neat-looking
34 Not quite a carpet
35 Advertising pieces
37 "Cakes and _____"
38 "The Addams Family" cousin
39 Fourchée or Latin design
40 NASA vehicle
41 Conceit
42 Tramples
44 Mischievous child
45 Degree of completion
47 Like much dietary food
49 Cover
50 Drive-time news source
51 Basic piano chord
54 _____ de Janeiro
56 Study quickly
59 *"L'Etoile du Nord"* (The star of the north)
61 Therefore
62 Surrounded by
63 Retired
64 New York city
65 New Jersey's team
66 Prized possessions
67 Hotel choice

Down

1 PBS series
2 Ilmenite and cuprite
3 *"Al-Ki"* (By and by)
4 Go with
5 Affirmative word
6 Bribed
7 Opposite of "stoss"
8 Saucy girl
9 _____ of a gun!
10 Ship's flag
11 Stood
12 Kind of house or secret
13 Consults
19 Inventor Howe
24 Stomach, familiarly
25 Showed effect of a stimulus
26 _____ non grata
27 Cooked
28 Money spent
29 Hoofbeat sounds
30 Word misused for "fewer"
31 "Eureka" (I have found it)
32 Muslim council
33 Be alluring
36 Vexes
42 Sarcastic
43 Approval
46 Large antelopes
48 Fine detail
50 Paths
51 Ness, e.g.
52 Hoar frost
53 _____ for keeps
54 Dressing gown
55 Target of gossip
57 CPA concern
58 Flesh
60 Droop
61 Whazzat?

Ono-Motto-Peia by Mel Rosen

Across

1 Bounders
5 Soothing lotions
10 Lhasa _____
14 Trumpet
15 Use
16 Part of speech
17 Best-selling cookie
18 Formal pronouncements
19 Swiss artist
20 Part 1 of a W.C. Fields line
23 This planet
24 Forest denizen
25 Kindergarten break
28 Gas: Comb. form
31 Talks nonsense
33 More of the line
38 Count of jazz
39 Dover's fish
40 Musical finales
43 Stead
44 Frog's call
46 More of line
48 Making amends
51 King's topper
52 Blushing
53 Bird with a weird cry
55 Famous furrier
60 End of the line
64 Fiscal period
66 On the wagon
67 Tell _____ the judge!
68 Against: Pref.
69 Noted 18th-century mathematician
70 Husky's load
71 Sharp
72 Hitchcock's "The 39 _____"
73 Withered

Down

1 Opted
2 Major artery
3 Dismal
4 Express contempt
5 Ordered
6 Tel _____, Israel
7 Added booze
8 _____ conure; parrot's cousin
9 Dragon dispatcher
10 Singer/songwriter Paul
11 Samoa, Tonga, and so on, loosely
12 Take to court
13 _____ up; leading
21 Certain Asian
22 Small amount
26 Unfamiliar
27 Quasi-
29 List ender
30 Greek letter
32 Crooner Jerry
33 Madison or Levant
34 Strong point
35 Sluice's cousin
36 Break of a habit
37 Commercial notices
41 GP's org.
42 Editor's disclaimer
45 Piper's wear
47 Regan's dad
49 Unidentified sounds
50 Escaped
54 Distinguished
56 69 Across's nationality
57 Baron, for example
58 Playful mammal
59 _____ Island
61 Isle of poesy
62 Second in command
63 Slips up
64 Chatter
65 Chemical ending

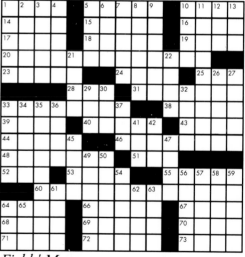

Fields' Motto by Mel Rosen

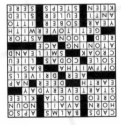